LEARN MUSIC LEARN MUSIC LEARN MUSIC LEARN MUSIC LEARN MUSIC LEARN MUSIC
D1032974
MUSIC LEARN MUSIC
LEARN MUSIC

ACTIVE MINDS

LEARN MUSIC

My First Interactive Songbook

Publications International, Ltd.

Puppy starts his music adventure at the train station. "Toot toot," goes the train. Pig hums a tune. Skunk blows his whistle. It is time to go!

TICKETS

DOWN BY THE STATION

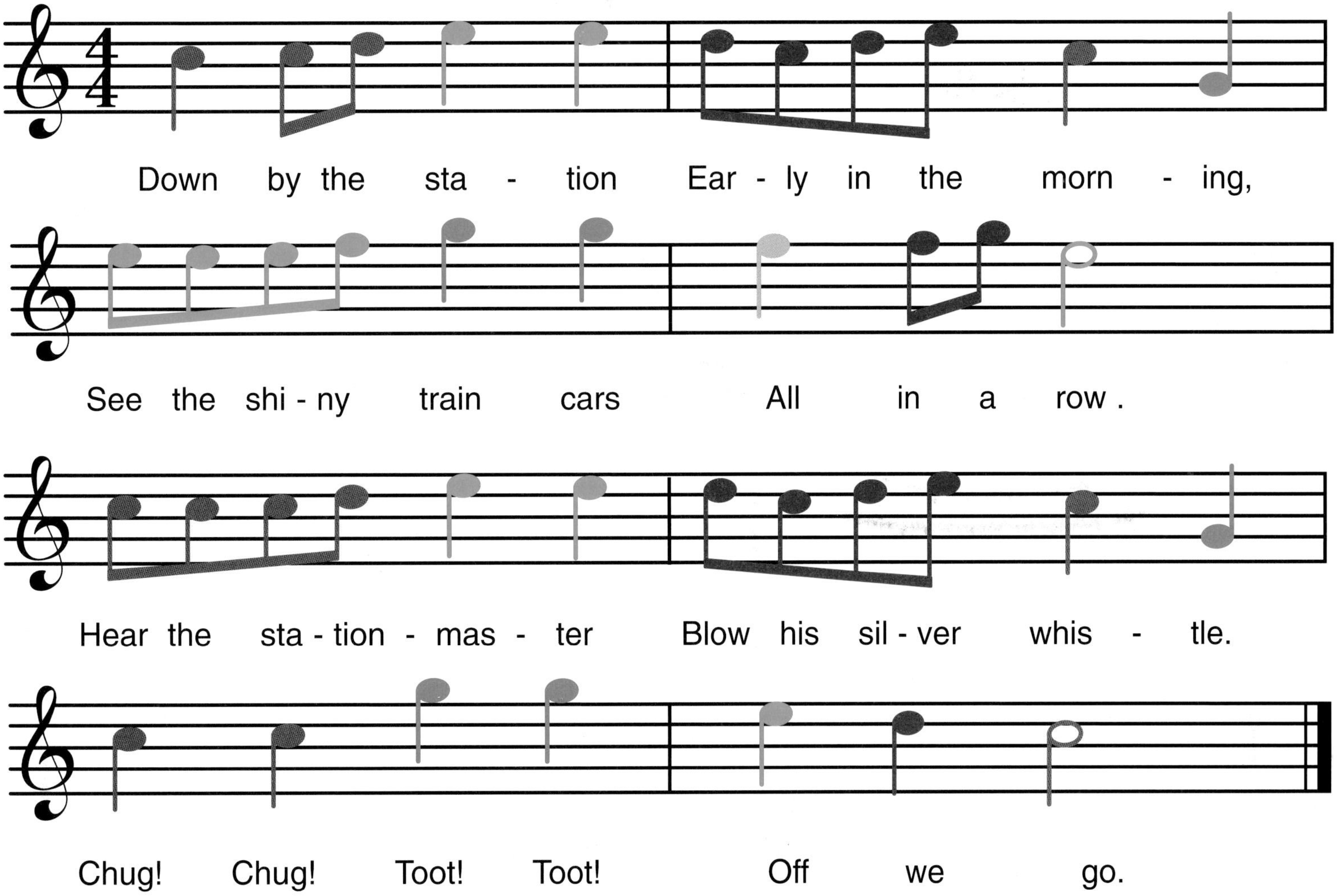
Down by the sta - tion Ear - ly in the morn - ing,
See the shi - ny train cars All in a row.
Hear the sta - tion - mas - ter Blow his sil - ver whis - tle.
Chug! Chug! Toot! Toot! Off we go.

OLD MACDONALD

Old Mac-Don-ald had a farm. E-I-E-I-O! And
on his farm he had some chickens. E-I-E-I-O! With a
cluck-cluck here And a cluck-cluck there, Here a cluck, there a cluck, Ev-'ry-where a cluck-cluck,
Old Mac-Don-ald had a farm. E-I-E-I-O!

Puppy stops at a farm to enjoy some country music. Pig plays a washboard. Hippo plays a banjo. Mouse and Hen dance to a down-home beat.

In the big city, Puppy visits a concert hall. He listens to Hippo sing like an opera star. Mouse and Hen play their instruments along with Hippo's song.

A-TISKET, A-TASKET

A - tis - ket, a - tas - ket, A
green and yel - low bas - ket, I wrote a let - ter to my love And
on the way I dropped it. I dropped it. I dropped it. And
on the way I dropped it. A lit - tle girl she came a - long And
put it in her pock - et.

THE MORE WE GET TOGETHER

The more we get to - geth - er, To -
geth - er, to - geth - er, The more we get to-
geth - er, The hap - pi - er we'll be. For
your friends are my friends, And my friends are
your friends. The more we get to - geth - er, The
hap - pi - er we'll be!

Puppy meets his friends on a mountaintop to play a polka tune. Pig's accordion makes high sounds. Tiger's tuba makes low sounds.

When the band comes marching by, Puppy leads the music with his baton. He is the drum major. Puppy's band marches in time to the music they play.

WHEN THE BAND COMES MARCHING BY

Oh, when the band, Oh, when the
band, Oh, when the band comes
march - ing by, Oh, how I
want to be in that num - ber,
Oh, when the band comes march - ing
by.

ROW ROW ROW YOUR BOAT

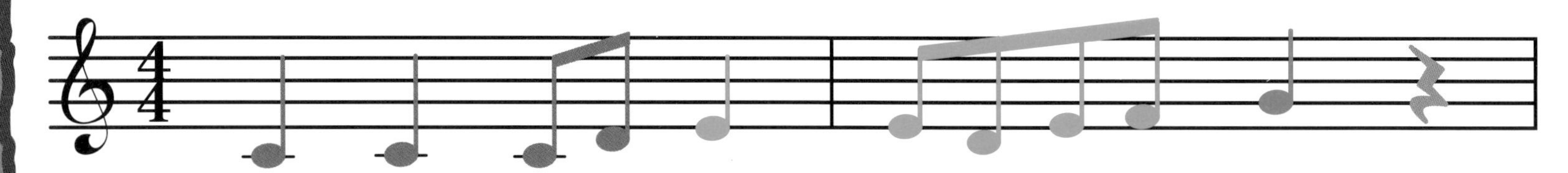

Row, row, row your boat, Gent - ly down the stream.

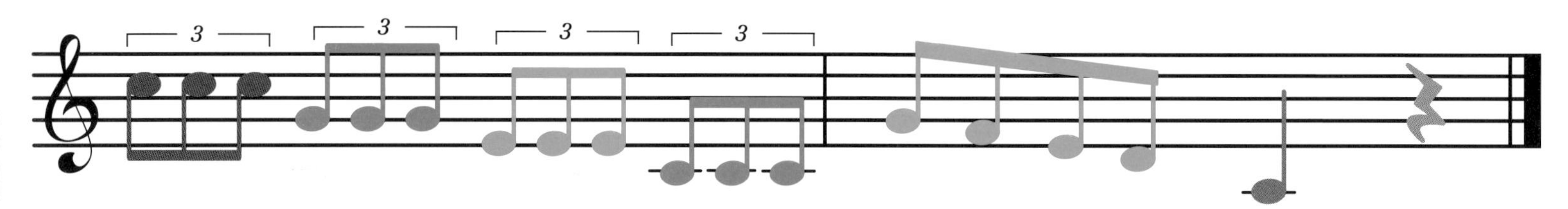

3 3 3 3
Mer -ri - ly, mer - ri - ly, mer - ri - ly, mer - ri -ly Life is but a dream.

Puppy and his friends sway to an island beat. Bunny shakes maracas. Hippo strums a ukulele. With Pig on steel drums, everyone wants to stand up and hula!

Riding through the desert, Puppy sings a Western song. He plays guitar. His horse plays harmonica. Guitar and harmonica make Puppy's song sound just right.

MY DARLIN' CLEMENTINE

Oh, my dar - lin', Oh, my dar - lin', Oh, my
dar - lin' Clem - en - tine, I am rid - ing home to
meet you In the moon - light, Clem - en - tine.

EENSY WEENSY SPIDER

The Een - sy Ween - sy Spi - der went
up the wa - ter spout. Down came the rain and
washed the spi - der out. Out came the sun and
dried up all the rain. Then the Een - sy Ween - sy Spi - der went
up the spout a - gain.

Puppy's next stop is a jazz café. Hippo plays a cool bass. Bunny sings and snaps her fingers. Puppy taps his bongos to keep the jazzy beat.

Puppy comes on stage for an all-star rock-and-roll show. Skunk sings the solo. Electric guitars play loud and fast. Bunny plays drums all night long.

TWINKLE, TWINKLE, LITTLE STAR

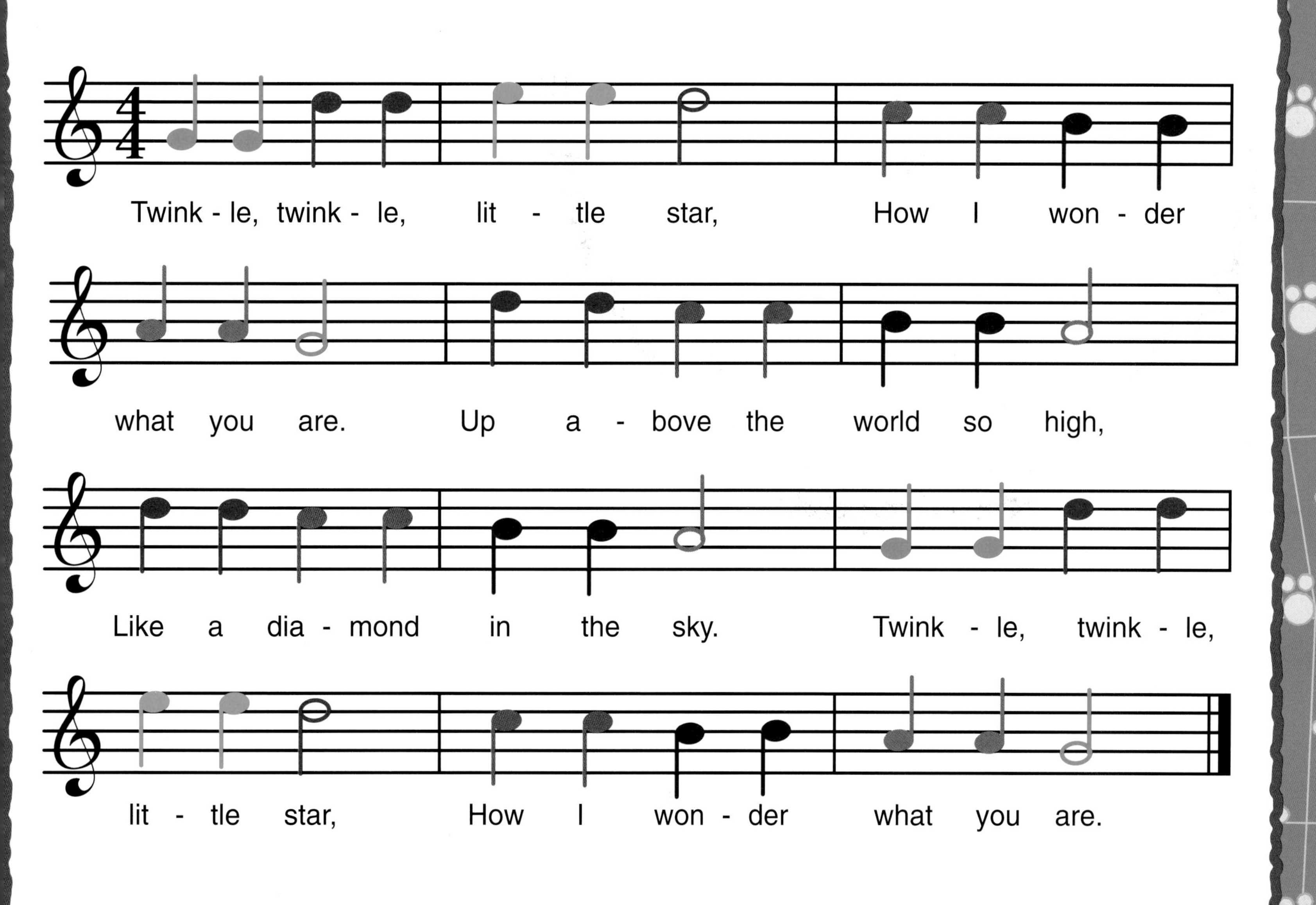

Twink - le, twink - le, lit - tle star, How I won - der
what you are. Up a - bove the world so high,
Like a dia - mond in the sky. Twink - le, twink - le,
lit - tle star, How I won - der what you are.

I'VE BEEN TRAVELING ON THE RAILROAD

I've been travel-ing on the rail - road All the live - long
day. I've been travel-ing on the rail - road Just to
pass the time a - way. Can't you hear the whis - tle
blow - ing? Rise up so ear-ly in the morn.
Can't you hear the cap-tain shout - ing, "Di - nah, blow your
horn!"